C000264424

Looking back
with ME

LIVING FOR A QUARTER OF A CENTURY WITH THE
NEUROIMMUNE DISORDER ME
(MYALGIC ENCEPHALOMYELITIS)

© Hazel Stapleton 2017
First printed 2017

ISBN 978-1-84625-582-3

British Library Cataloguing in Publication Data available

Unless otherwise indicated, Scripture quotations in this publication
are from the King James (Authorized) Version (KJV), Crown copyright.

Published by Day One Publications
Ryelands Road, Leominster, HR6 8NZ
☎ 01568 613 740 FAX 01568 611 473
email—sales@dayone.co.uk
web site—www.dayone.co.uk

Cover illustration by Kathryn Chedgzoy
Printed by TJ International Ltd

I appreciated reading Hazel's witness to the Lord's grace in saving her, and all His subsequent dealings, which comes over very well and much to His glory. I trust the information given about ME may open the eyes of people to take this condition seriously, especially the medical profession.

Rev. John Thackway, Pastor, Holywell Evangelical Church

It was most moving to read of the way the Lord has led Hazel these past years, and I was richly blessed by her regular reminders that God is sovereign in every detail of our lives.

Derek French, Elder, Hanney Chapel near Wantage

This book documents Hazel's life both before and since her illness. No, it isn't cheerful to read about a chronic illness and some of the difficulties both with diagnosis and in terms of management of the condition. Yet Hazel is a Christian and is clear that she has a hope greater than this life. Of course, this book is of relevance to people with ME, but it is also relevant to those of us who have been given many years of good health. It is easy to moan and forget to be thankful for this gift. It is encouraging to be reminded of the Lord and His promises.

Sarah Jones, former consultant physician, London

To my parents, Mark and Jean,
with thanks

*Hast thou not known? hast thou not heard, that
the everlasting God, the Lord, the Creator of the
ends of the earth, fainteth not, neither is weary? there is
no searching of his understanding.
He giveth power to the faint; and to them that have no
might he increaseth strength.
Even the youths shall faint and be weary, and the
young men shall utterly fall:
But they that wait upon the Lord shall renew their
strength; they shall mount up with wings as eagles;
they shall run, and not be weary; and they shall walk,
and not faint.*
(Isaiah 40:28–31)

*In my experience, [ME] is one of the most disabling
diseases that I care for, far exceeding HIV disease
except for the terminal stages.*

(Dr Daniel L Peterson, Introduction to Research and
Clinical Conference, Fort Lauderdale, Florida, October
1994; published in 'Introduction', *Journal of Chronic
Fatigue Syndrome* 1, no. 3–4 [1995]: 123–125)

Contents

*T*he Lord *is my*
shepherd; I shall not
want.
(Psalm 23:1)

⟜

*I*n 2004, *a randomized clinical trial found that*
'*In comparison with other chronic illnesses such*
as multiple sclerosis, end-stage renal disease and
heart disease, patients with [ME] show markedly
higher levels of disability'.
(*American Journal of Occupational Therapy* 58
[2004]: 35–43)

Introduction

Why another book about ME? That is a good question. My main reason for writing is the continuing lack of understanding surrounding ME. Even now, after so many years of illness, I still find that some people—even those who know me—are unaware of the impact and serious nature of ME: that at its worst it can be fatal. I get comments such as 'I hope you're keeping well'; 'isn't ME just about feeling tired?'; or 'surely you could exercise yourself better?' (when exercise is actually one of the worst things that a person with ME could do). So, as much as I really don't like writing about myself, I felt that putting my own experiences of ME down on paper—and comparing them with how I was before my illness began—would be the best way to try to get across what this illness is really like. Hopefully, reading about an individual's experience of ME rather than a list of medical facts will help people to understand more about this devastating disease and the effects it has on people's lives.

Part of the problem, in the UK at least, is due to the continued portrayal of ME as a psychological problem, in spite of the overwhelming evidence to the contrary. After all, ME has been listed by the World Health Organization as a neurological condition since 1969, so it's about time that it was treated like one! A few years ago, an ME researcher in America, Dr Suzanne Vernon, stated that there were over 5,000 peer-reviewed articles in the biomedical literature about ME—yet much of the evidence of the biomedical nature of ME has been suppressed or ignored in the UK, probably resulting in long-term harm to many patients who are incorrectly 'treated' by being told they need to exercise or undertake some kind of behavioural therapy. Imagine what would happen if MS or Motor Neurone Disease (MND) sufferers were told they needed 'therapy' as their first-line, or indeed only, treatment option? There would be an outcry, and rightly so. It should be the same with ME.

Whilst it is true that ME is a neurological condition, it is also true to describe it as a multi-system failure, as research has found that damage or problems affect virtually every part and system of the body. No amount of exercise or therapy is going to put those problems right—and studies have repeatedly found such to be harmful, particularly when it comes to 'graded exercise therapy'.

It is for this reason that I am writing about my own experiences of ME over the last twenty-five years. I hope that this will be of some help, whether to others with ME or to those without it, to help them to understand a little more about the illness and its effects on daily life and living.

*T*rust in the LORD *with all thine heart; and
lean not unto thine own understanding.
In all thy ways acknowledge him, and he shall
direct thy paths.*
(Proverbs 3:5–6)

*M*E *in adults is associated with measurable
changes in the central nervous system
and autonomic function and injury to the
cardiovascular, endocrine and other organs and
systems. The belief that [ME] is a psychological
illness is the error of our time.*
(Dr Byron Hyde, 'The Complexities of Diagnosis',
in Leonard A. Jason, Patricia A. Fennell and Renée
R. Taylor [eds.], *The Handbook of Chronic Fatigue
Syndrome* [Hoboken, NJ: John Wiley & Sons, 2003]).

How it all started

I can still remember it quite well. It was Sunday, 5 August 1990. I was looking out of the window of my room on the fourth floor of the nurses' home at Llandough hospital, just south of Cardiff, watching my parents leave. Knowing that I had to be there by the Sunday evening, we had driven to Cardiff during the afternoon, had a picnic tea, gone to the evening service at the church I hoped to attend, and then found our way to the nurses' home. It felt a bit strange watching Mum and Dad drive off, but I was looking forward to starting my nurse training, living away from home for the first time, making new friends, learning new skills.

The next morning my fellow students and I had to be up early to catch the minibus to take us to the School of Nursing at the University Hospital of Wales (UHW), which was the other side of Cardiff from Llandough. Most of my group were actually living at the UHW, but for some unknown reason a few of us were housed in the nurses' home at Llandough. I had been to the UHW the previous year for an interview, but had not even heard of Llandough until I was told I would be living there!

The first week was really just to get to know the others in the group, get to know the tutors (who all seemed quite nice), learn a bit about what to expect during the course, and hopefully start to find our way around. On the Monday, less than twenty-four hours after arriving, I discovered that there was a Christian Union group at Llandough hospital which was meeting that very evening, so I got to know a few of the Christians at the hospital right from the start. The week went well until the Friday afternoon, when we went to the Occupational Health (OH) department to discuss certain health issues and to have various vaccinations. Happily— or so I thought—the only one I needed was the first of the course of three Hepatitis B vaccines.

Chapter 1

I had previously had other vaccinations without any problems, but around ten minutes after having that first Hep B vaccine, I collapsed. The staff in the Occupational Health department were not very helpful (to put it mildly), so it was left to a few of the people from my group to help get me back to my room at Llandough. I was thankful that one of the ambulance cadets who lived on the same floor offered to keep an eye on me overnight—I had knocked my head as I collapsed, so as well as having had a bad reaction to the vaccine, I was concussed.

Normally under such circumstances, I have no doubt that Mum and Dad would have rushed over from home to make sure that I was OK. Unfortunately, they were away at the time, cooking for a large beach mission team in Scarborough. However, a couple from the church in Cardiff very kindly put me up in their home, even though they didn't really know me. Their GP came out to see me, confirming that I had had a bad reaction to the vaccine and was suffering from concussion, and saying that there was very little I could do about it, except to wait for it to wear off. For the first few days all I wanted to do was sleep, so Mum and Dad made the decision to leave the beach mission in Scarborough and take me back home. The team leader assured them that they would be driving home 'on prayer rather than on petrol'.

I was unwell for five weeks after that first Hepatitis B vaccination. Looking back, it was like a 'mini ME'—not that I knew anything about ME then—with my main symptoms being an overwhelming exhaustion and lack of energy, muscle pain and balance problems. However, I made a good recovery, but, as I had missed more than five days during the first two months of training, I was told that I couldn't rejoin my nursing group; I would have to restart the course completely. Fortunately there was a space available at the end of September, so I didn't have very long to wait.

It was just at this time that the style of nurse training was changing. Up until this time, the training had taken place mainly on the wards, with a couple of weeks 'in school' every few weeks; it was soon to change to the other way around, mainly in the classroom with placements on various wards. The group I was to join at the end of September was the final group of the old style, on-the-ward training, which I was relieved about. I couldn't see—and still can't see—how it is possible to learn to be a nurse whilst spending most of the time sitting in a classroom. Although it is the method now in use, it wouldn't surprise me if sooner or later it changes back to the old way of training.

During those few weeks back at home we tried to find out a little about what could have happened with the vaccine, causing me to collapse, but we didn't really get anywhere. Mum spoke to one doctor at the Occupational Health department who simply said that no one became ill following any of their vaccinations, and that was that! A doctor who saw me about ten days after the incident was amazed at how little the staff at the OH department had done when I collapsed—particularly that I had not been seen by a doctor and no observations had been taken. This was a bit annoying, and didn't help in trying to find out what had happened, but as I had by this time recovered I wasn't worried and just tried to focus on restarting my course.

*B*e strong and of a good courage, fear not, nor
be afraid of them: for the LORD thy God, he
*it is that doth go with thee; he will not fail thee,
nor forsake thee.*
(Deuteronomy 31:6)

*W*hen the Chief Medical Officer's Report on ME
*was released in January 2002, the CMO for
England Professor Sir Liam Donaldson said that ME
'should be classed as a chronic condition with long
term effects on health, alongside other illnesses such as
multiple sclerosis and motor neurone disease'.*
(Quoted from 'M.E. Treatment "Must Improve"', 11
January 2002, BBC News website, http://news.bbc.
co.uk/1/hi/health/1755070.stm)

Chapter 2

Problems at the beginning

Things hadn't gone quite to plan when I was born: I arrived ten weeks early, weighing just 2 lb 10 oz, so I was rather a worry to my parents from day one! As a result of my early appearance I spent the first two months of my life in an incubator in a Special Care Baby Unit. There were no facilities back then for parents to stay with their babies, so Mum and Dad travelled to the hospital each day to see me. Other relatives were not allowed in.

Many premature babies, especially in those days, developed both short- and long-term problems due to having been born so early. The most common short-term problem was—and I would imagine probably still is—breathing difficulties, due to under-developed lungs. Long-term problems could include various forms of brain damage, neurological disorders such as cerebral palsy, intestinal problems, hearing loss, and so on. I was fortunate and did not appear to have any noticeable side-effects from being born so early, and the only problem that developed during my childhood years that is thought to be linked to my early birth was my being a bit uncoordinated. Mum says that I used to trip myself up or fall over my own feet, but that was nothing compared with the difficulties some children and their families went through.

However, thinking about it now, after being seriously ill for so long, is it possible that my being born so prematurely could in some way have contributed to all my years of ill-health? This is something I have often wondered about, and I do believe that it is highly likely that it is at least a factor. One doctor I saw some years ago definitely believed that my being born prematurely and developing ME—albeit nearly nineteen years apart—were undoubtedly linked. He thought that my adrenal glands in particular would not have developed properly; there is a big cross-over in the symptoms of ME and adrenal insufficiency, and I do have adrenal problems.

*The eternal God is thy refuge, and
underneath are the everlasting arms.*
(Deuteronomy 33:27)

*Our patients are terribly ill, misunderstood, and
suffer at the hands of a poorly informed medical
establishment and society.*
(Professor Nancy Klimas, University of Miami,
American Association for Chronic Fatigue Syndrome
In-coming Presidential Address, Co-Cure, 21 March
2005; from Archives of Co-Cure, https://listserv.nodak.
edu/archives/co-cure.html)

Starting again

At the end of September 1990 I returned to the nurses' home at Llandough. I was to have a different room, but it was still on the fourth floor—which did at least give me a good view looking towards the Bristol Channel. The few friends I knew from my previous group who lived there were very welcoming and wanted to know all about what had happened to me. I then found that there were four people from my new group, in addition to myself, living at Llandough—one of whom, in the room opposite mine, was a Christian and came from the same area in North Somerset as me!

It was strange starting again, listening to all the introductory week talks for the second time. However, all went well and on the Friday afternoon I made a point of avoiding the Occupational Health department! Unbelievably—all the more so looking back now—I was informed that I had to finish the course of three Hepatitis B vaccinations, as the 'powers that be' did not believe that the first one could have made me ill. I decided to put off doing so for as long as possible.

We had eight weeks in the classroom, travelling each day to the School of Nursing at the UHW. We were given something of a crash course in anatomy and physiology—not too difficult for those of us who had just left school having studied science subjects, but a bit tough for the members of our group who were starting their training after a break from studying. We were also taught some basic practical skills—making beds, giving injections, taking blood pressures, doing dressings—mainly practising on each other and plastic models, with a few visits to wards.

After the eight weeks we had a two-month placement on a ward. My ward was at Llandough, so no getting up early to catch the minibus each day for a while! It was a medical ward specializing in chest problems—asthma, bronchitis, chronic lung and breathing problems, and so on. The sister on the ward was soon to retire. She was very much of the 'old school' and ruled the roost. Everyone—doctors, nurses, other staff, medical students and we nursing students, who were the lowest of the low—had to obey her every word. Yes, she was strict, but at the same time we learnt a lot from her. Maybe it would be helpful to trainee nurses today to have such nursing sisters!

During this time I was able to attend church. Living at Llandough, I was quite a way from the church I wanted to attend—Heath Evangelical Church—but a lady who belonged to the church and lived in Penarth kindly offered to pick me up; she assured me that driving past the hospital was only a short detour for her.

When we started working on the wards it wasn't easy to attend services or mid-week meetings regularly, due to working shifts and some Sundays, but it worked out pretty well. The couple in the church who had looked after me when I was ill after the first vaccination worked with overseas students, so I attended their Sunday afternoon meetings when I could. It was good to meet with folk from numerous different countries and backgrounds—not something that often happened at my church back home.

However, there was still one unresolved problem—completing the course of three Hepatitis B vaccines, something which I was reminded about at regular intervals. I sought advice from a local GP, but as this particular vaccine was relatively new, there didn't seem to be much information available on side-effects. This GP's view was that, if I did have any problems, they wouldn't be any worse than those I had had the first time and would probably not be as bad, so I should therefore go ahead and have the second injection. I wasn't particularly happy about this, but as an eighteen-year-old student nurse, how could I argue with such medical advice? So, on 8 February 1991, I had the second vaccination. A friend came with me to make sure that I was all right, but thankfully I didn't collapse. However, within under an hour—probably only around thirty minutes—I started to feel unwell. My sense of balance went haywire and I couldn't stand up without holding onto something. Strange as it may seem, though, I wasn't very worried. I hadn't collapsed, and I had heard of other people feeling a bit 'off' for a day or two following a vaccination, so I went home to get over it, thinking that I would be OK again after a few days. How wrong I was!

*Commit thy way unto the LORD;
trust also in him, and he shall
bring it to pass.*
(Psalm 37:5)

⁓

*The evidence is now so strong that
ME/CFS [Chronic Fatigue Syndrome]
is a multisystem neuro-immune disease
that it becomes intellectually embarrassing
for anyone to continue to consider it to be
a psychosomatic disorder.*
(The Countess of Mar, 'Countess of Mar's Letter to
Author', ME Research UK, posted 18 June 2015, http://
www.meresearch.org.uk/news/countess-of-mar-letter/)

A healthy childhood

Having survived being born ten weeks prematurely with very few problems, the rest of my early years were unremarkable and healthy. I had measles as a baby, and my brother Tim and I caught the 'normal' childhood illnesses, such as chickenpox, as they did the rounds; there was nothing to suggest any future problems.

We had (and still have) a close family. Dad, now retired, worked for many years in the NHS in hospital finance. Mum, also retired, was a trained nurse. She had planned to study midwifery in Edinburgh, but it was at that time that she met Dad, so she never got to Edinburgh! Mum and Dad had both become Christians early in their lives, and Tim and I were brought up to attend church on a regular basis. We were also taught from the Bible at home, and Mum used to read to us from Christian books. I particularly enjoyed hearing of the lives of well-known missionaries such as Hudson Taylor, William Carey and Mary Slessor. I think that it was listening to Mum reading these biographies that started my interest in missionary work—I thought that maybe I would be able to do something exciting like that one day!

Some people are able to give a precise time and date for when they became Christians; I cannot. I believe that I was saved when I was around seven or eight years of age, but I can't be more exact. That used to worry me, but the words of a friend were helpful, and I've never forgotten them. She said to imagine that you are travelling by train, going through a tunnel, from one country to another. At some point during the journey you cross the border, but, being in the tunnel, you don't know exactly when that happens. However, when you come out of the tunnel, you know that you are in the new country—and that is how it is with those of us whom God has saved, by His grace, but who don't know exactly when it happened. We know that we are Christians; we just can't give an exact time as to when the great change took place.

At church Tim and I attended the Sunday school, known as Adventurers, which included going on the yearly camp away from home for a couple of nights—I remember some very cold weekends away! The church we belonged to also had an annual holiday club which had become quite well known in the village. I remember one year, when the theme was the life of Daniel, about 200 children came along. The holiday club at that church is still going, but with considerably fewer children—a sign of the times, no doubt.

As well as the privilege of having Christian parents, my brother and I were also blessed with four Christian grandparents. Grandma and Grandpa (for many years a Baptist minister), Dad's parents, lived not far away, and when we were about seven or eight, Gran and Grandad, Mum's parents, moved from their home in Liverpool to live in a flat just a couple of minutes' walk from where we lived. Surrounded by grandparents, we had many years of family occasions marking birthdays, wedding anniversaries, Christmas, and so on.

Neither Mum nor Dad could ever be described as 'sporty', but we were encouraged to learn to swim and took part in sports lessons at school. The family holidays that I recall most clearly were to North Devon, as well as Cornwall and the New Forest. So, with family life, attending church, going to school, games, playing with local friends and holidays, I was certainly fit and active. There were no signs of any of the health problems that were to come later on.

*B*ut my God shall supply all your need
*according to his riches in glory by Christ
Jesus.*
(Philippians 4:19)

*A*n ME patient 'feels effectively the same every day
*as an AIDS patient feels two weeks before death;
the only difference is that the symptoms can go on for
never-ending decades'.*
Professor Mark Loveless, Head of the AIDS and ME/
CFS Clinic at Oregon Health Sciences University,
Congressional Briefing, 1995

What is wrong with me?

Feeling very unwell, I arrived back at home after the second Hepatitis B vaccination. As well as the balance problems, within just twenty-four hours all the symptoms I had experienced after the first injection had returned, most noticeably the muscle pain and exhaustion. I expected to be better after a few days, then after a few weeks—but it didn't happen. In fact, the opposite was true: I got worse.

At first I remained under the care of my GP in Cardiff, and it was him who, after three months, first suggested that I might have ME. He did lots of blood tests and was very sympathetic to my situation, but travelling for over an hour each way when feeling very unwell to see my GP was not sustainable, so I re-registered with my GP back at home.

However, with Mum and Dad's help, I had to return to Cardiff in order to clear my room—for the second time. I met with my tutor at the School of Nursing and was assured of a place in a future group of student nurses if I wanted it, as soon as I was well enough to take it up. That never happened.

The worst thing about that time was not knowing what was wrong with me. At one time I more or less convinced myself that I must have some sort of brain tumour, with being so unwell for so long and clearly getting worse. I wasn't severely affected by whatever it was, but I was in no way well enough to work even on a part-time basis. I could walk to the local shops—although that wasn't easy due to the balance problems and pain—but I had to go to bed for a few hours each afternoon to get through the rest of the day.

We had some neighbours who went swimming once a week, so I decided to go with them, thinking that taking up some form of exercise such as swimming would help me to get better more quickly. It didn't. I ended up crashing out after getting home from swimming, and just about recovering sufficiently to go back again the following week. I didn't last many weeks! Mum and I also used to go into town to do some shopping, but the result was much the same as with swimming. I would get home and just lie in bed or on the settee for days afterwards, trying to recover. With hindsight, I would say that walking round the shops and going swimming (or taking any form of exercise) was probably the worst thing I could have done, and it probably contributed to my condition becoming chronic and severe. But I didn't know that back then.

Thankfully, my GP was sympathetic, did lots more blood tests, but still didn't really know what was wrong with me—other than 'probably ME'. She referred me to an NHS consultant neurologist. More blood tests, examinations, a brain scan, and finally, ten months after the second vaccination, a diagnosis: ME, Myalgic Encephalomyelitis. What a relief! At long last I knew what was wrong with me. I could now find out about my illness and see what I needed to do in order to get better. Or could I?

My relief at having a name for my illness was short-lived. Although I had no Internet access back then to look things up and get in touch with other sufferers, it didn't take me long to realize that ME is not a good illness to have! Yes, it had been listed by the World Health Organization as a neurological condition alongside conditions such as MS and MND since 1969, yet many people, especially members of the medical profession, did not believe in its existence (and still don't), and if they did, they thought it was some kind of psychological problem.

It was a confusing time. I knew that I was physically ill, something that I and my parents never doubted. But I was getting worse, not better, developing more symptoms and more problems. I finally had a name for my illness, but there was apparently no treatment that could be given or advice to be offered.

During my final appointment with the neurologist I asked him for advice. He firmly believed ME to be a physical, neurological illness, but his only reply was, 'Have you thought of alternative medicine?'

*Casting all your care
upon him; for he careth
for you.*
(1 Peter 5:7)

*I hope you are not saying that [ME] patients are
not as ill as HIV patients. I split my clinical time
between the two illnesses, and I can tell you that if
I had to choose between the two illnesses I would
rather have HIV.*
(Professor Nancy Klimas, then Professor of
Medicine, Microbiology and Immunology, at the
University of Miami, writing in the *New York
Times*, 15 October 2009)

Beach missions and exams

Moving at the age of eleven from my local junior school, which had around 300 pupils, to the comprehensive, with 1,500, was something of a shock to the system. There was no question as to which school to go to, as we often hear about nowadays on the news; if you lived in a certain place, you knew which school you were going to, and that was that. The comprehensive school was about seven miles from where we lived, so there were hundreds of us who had to be bussed in every day. During the winters we used to listen avidly to the local radio station in case there was a chance that we couldn't get to school because of snow—but it rarely happened! I was there for seven years, doing both GCSEs and A-levels, and it was a good school; I believe it is now an academy.

One interesting thing, considering what was to come, was that in the sixth form, as well as studying academic subjects, we had to do something practical. We were given a choice of three things: first aid (which I had already done in the Red Cross), photography (not interested) or typing—so I ended up doing typing. Back then, I thought that it was a complete waste of time, as I was going to be a nurse; why would I want to learn to type? Yet I can now see the Lord's over-ruling even in this. He knows the end from the beginning and knew that I would become ill and very dependent on email and the Internet. I can now say that I am thankful for those typing lessons!

When I was fourteen I attended a mid-week meeting at our church which was being taken by a speaker from the Lord's Day Observance Society who had brought various books and other pieces of literature for us to look at. After the meeting I spotted a magazine entitled *The Lord's Day* produced by Young Life and I took it home to read. There was a page in it about beach missions, and straight away I thought that was something I would like to get involved with. I wrote off to the beach missions office for further details, but was saddened to discover that the minimum age to join a beach team was fifteen and I was only fourteen. However, the following year I spent two weeks on a beach mission in Paignton, South Devon. I didn't know anyone on the team in advance, so it was a bit nerve-wracking at first, but I did enjoy it, although it was hard work. Ever since then I have kept in touch with the team leader and his wife, who are now working with the Open Air Mission, and they have been a great help and support over the years.

The following year I again booked up for two weeks on the team at Paignton, along with a couple of others I had met the previous year, and my brother Tim, who was now fifteen, also joined the team. But it didn't end there. Thinking that we would both be away for two weeks, Mum and Dad had planned two weeks' holiday for themselves—one week away in Cornwall, the second week having a holiday at home. However, during our first week in Paignton, it became clear that we did not have a cook for the second week. I knew Mum and Dad were both due to be free that week, so, with permission from the team leader, I left a phone message for them at the place where they were staying (no mobile phones then!) and, to cut a long story short, they joined Tim, me and the rest of the team for the second week in Paignton, with them doing the cooking. It was quite an introduction to beach missions for them!

It actually turned out to be the start of a long association with beach missions, as a few years later Dad was asked to be the beach mission centre leader for St Ives in Cornwall. The office was up in Leeds, and as we were in North Somerset, they thought that Cornwall was just down the road from us! Coordinating the beach missions in St Ives and looking after the mission house down there was something that Mum and Dad kept up for fifteen years, resulting in numerous trips to Cornwall and our getting to know quite a lot of people and the area very well. We still try to follow the work, but now from the sidelines.

It was in April 1989 that Tim and I were both baptized, a happy occasion when we were joined by various family, friends and neighbours who came to the service and heard the gospel. Many of them also came back home to have lunch with us afterwards. Later that year, Grandpa died very suddenly. The funeral service was held at the church where we had been baptized and where Grandpa had years earlier been the minister; there were hundreds of people at the service. After that, I spent most of my weekends staying with Grandma, trying to help her as much as I could. She lived for over sixteen years without Grandpa (they had been childhood sweethearts and used to walk home from Sunday school together holding hands!), and she was a great source of help, support and comfort to me, particularly during the early years of my illness (before she herself became unwell).

Why do I mention all these things? To show that life was busy: going on beach missions, studying for A-levels, church activities, being a member of the Red Cross, helping Grandma, learning to drive and passing my test, applying and being accepted for nurse training in Cardiff. I would think that at this time I was probably the most fit and active I had ever been, and I was looking forward to starting nursing. Again, there was nothing to indicate that all of this was soon to end with the breakdown of my health.

*T*he LORD *is my rock, and my fortress, and my deliverer; my God, my strength, in whom I will trust.*
(Psalm 18:2)

*T*here *is no word in the English lexicon that describes the lack of stamina, the paucity of energy [and] the absolute malaise that accompanies this illness.*
(Charles Lapp, Professor of Community and Family Medicine at Duke University, USA, Co-Cure, 3 June 2004)

A slow decline

It was December 1991. I now had a diagnosis of ME, Myalgic Encephalomyelitis, a neurological disorder, but the consultant had offered no hope and given me no information. I wasn't bed-bound or house-bound, and over the following months and years nothing dramatic happened—just a gradual worsening of my health.

Mum and Dad were, as they always have been, an amazing help and support, but trying to explain to family and friends this mysterious illness, which at the start I knew very little about, was not easy. At the beginning my knowledge of ME consisted of thinking that it was 'something to do with a virus'. Most cases of ME do indeed start following some sort of viral illness—although there are quite a few of us for whom it started with a vaccination—but such scant knowledge was not very helpful.

A close friend saw an advert in a magazine for an ME support charity and she sent off for an information pack for me. It was helpful to have some facts about the illness and leaflets that I could pass on to others, but even so, there were still a few friends and family members who were rather sceptical. A couple of times I attended a local ME support group, but I found it rather depressing, with most of the people a lot older than me (probably about the age I am now!). They spent most of the time talking about their symptoms and how bad they were feeling, and there were no other Christians present, so I didn't keep up with going to the group.

A few of the people I had been at school with did stay in touch for a while after we left, but once I became ill, it got difficult to keep up the contact. Whenever they arranged to meet up, I wasn't well enough to go along. On the couple of occasions that they came to see me, the conversation wasn't easy; they were doing well in their studies, had done some travelling, all sorts of 'normal' things—and I had done nothing, apart from seeing my

GP or attending a hospital appointment! At this time I was still able to attend church, although the frequency with which I went to the meetings gradually declined. Even when I was first ill I didn't make it to all of the meetings, but at the start I did usually manage the Sunday evening services (I don't do mornings!) and occasionally the mid-week meeting. As a result, I think that many people in the church weren't really aware that I was ill; with my not being at all the meetings, some thought I had returned to nurse training!

A few months after becoming ill, I got in touch with a Christian lady we had known some years before and who was a trained medical herbalist. She really thought that she could help—and I have no doubt that herbal medicines can help with many different conditions—but I was unable to tolerate the various herbal concoctions that she suggested. I didn't know it at the time, but having problems tolerating medication, whether orthodox or complementary, synthetic or natural, is virtually a hallmark of ME and has been an increasing problem for me over the years.

Not having found any benefit in the herbal remedies, and not knowing that being unable to tolerate many kinds of medication would be an ongoing problem, I then got in touch with a consultant homeopathic physician who, like the herbalist, was also a Christian. He was a very nice person to talk to and was very supportive (he wrote excellent letters when I got into difficulties over disability benefits!), but sadly the medication he prescribed brought no relief. In fact, I reacted badly to everything he recommended. I had the 'aggravation' of symptoms, as they call it in homeopathic medicine, but I never got the improvement that is meant to come afterwards.

For just over seven years I experienced a gradual decline in health. The amount that I could do, the distances I could walk, all slowly got less, as did my walking speed! It wasn't that I lacked motivation or anything like that. I wanted to get better more than anything, but there seemed to be nothing that I could do to stop—or even slow down—the deterioration. Whatever those Hepatitis B vaccinations had done to my body, they had certainly caused a lot of damage, which became more obvious as my condition progressed—and it would become even more obvious in the coming years.

As well as trying both herbal and homeopathic medicines, I tried various diets that some ME sufferers had reportedly found helpful—gluten-free, dairy-free, yeast-and-sugar-free—but, again, they made no difference, apart from starting off a long-term interest in all things nutritional! I have come to see that nutrition is a much-neglected area of medicine, most medics having very little—if any—training in or understanding of it. I firmly believe that nutrition can play a big part in our health (or lack of it), especially in chronic illnesses.

*A*nd he said unto me, My grace is sufficient
for thee; for my strength is made perfect in
weakness.
(2 Corinthians 12:9)

⁓

*T*here is considerable evidence already that the
immune system is in a state of chronic activation
in many patients with [ME].
(Anthony Komaroff, Assistant Professor of Medicine,
Harvard Medical School: American Medical
Association Statement, Co-Cure, 17 July 2001)

Hopes for the future

I can't remember a time when I wasn't interested in medical things, and especially in nursing. I imagine that Mum being a trained nurse had something to do with it, but I always enjoyed learning about all things medical from programmes on television and from reading books.

Growing up, I had very little to do with hospitals (thankfully), apart from a minor operation for a squint when I was eight years old. I was kept on the children's ward in the eye hospital for two nights (it would probably be only for a few hours today!), and there was no option for parents to stay with their children. I don't remember much about it, except that it meant I was unable to go to the church holiday club and that my bed on the ward was next to a large fish tank, which I guess would be considered too unhygienic nowadays!

My interest in missionary work also grew over the years. At the age of nine I had started writing to a missionary couple and I kept in touch with them for many years. It was fascinating to hear about their lives in a totally different culture and climate from ours, and I had no doubt through my teens that I would end up working overseas after my nurse training, probably somewhere in east Africa.

Although that clearly has not happened, over the years since becoming ill I have had the privilege of corresponding with people working in numerous different countries. At first it was all done by letter, but now being able to keep in touch via email has made things a lot easier (and cheaper). I often think of how much missionaries from previous centuries, such as William Carey, would have appreciated email. Carey had to wait for many long and lonely months, with an ill wife and family, before he had any news from back home. Whilst emails and text messages can be abused, they can also be of great benefit, and I would encourage anyone who is ill, particularly those unable to get out very much, to correspond with people living and working in different parts of the world. Thanks to modern technology, today you can lie in bed and send and receive messages from people both at home and abroad.

I had hopes and plans for the future—including nursing, working abroad, wanting to get married and have a family—but none of them have worked out. Was I wrong to start nurse training, having been sure that it was what the Lord was guiding me into? If I had gone down another route, would I still have become ill?

I can't answer either question with 100 per cent certainty, but to answer the second question first: yes, I think it is very likely that, whatever route I went down (work, university or something else), my health would still have broken down at some point. If it hadn't been the Hepatitis B vaccine that started things off, I think something else would have done so instead, maybe a different vaccine or form of medication.

Was I right to start nurse training? Again, yes, I believe so. I have no doubt from the Bible that God does guide His people, and it was in my mind from very early on that I should do nurse training—something confirmed numerous times by the way things worked out as I grew up. God is over all things, and there are no accidents in anything that He does. So, yes, I do believe that it was His will—as was also, I believe, my getting ME and having to stop my training. The last twenty-five years have not been as I would have chosen, but my interest in medical things since an early age has certainly helped me to cope with ME, especially as I have tried to learn about it and help others with it. Obviously, I don't have all the answers; indeed, it frequently feels as if I don't have any answers—just lots of questions. Not until we reach heaven will we know the reasons for the things which have happened to us, but until then, although it may not seem like it, God is in control. He is sovereign. His purposes cannot be thwarted.

> And we know that all things work together for good to them that love God, to them who are the called according to his purpose.
>
> For whom he did foreknow, he also did predestinate to be conformed to the image of his Son, that he might be the firstborn among many brethren.
>
> (Romans 8:28–29)

The Lord *is good, a strong hold in the day
of trouble; and he knoweth them that trust
in him.*
(Nahum 1:7)

*The most seriously affected individuals may be
bed-ridden most or all of the time and can do
little or nothing for themselves. Recent research has
made it clear that the view that there were no specific
changes demonstrable in patients with ME has become
untenable.*
(Dr Derek Pheby, Director, Cancer Epidemiology
Research Unit, Bristol University: 'CFS: A Challenge
to the Clinical Professions', *Physiotherapy* 83, no. 2
[1997]: 53–56)

Severe ME and shrinking walls

With the slow decline in my health since I became ill you could say that I had been moderately affected by ME, but that was soon to change. In the summer of 1998 I went down with shingles for the first time—unusual in someone my age, but not so unusual in those who have problems with their immune system, as is the case with ME patients. Shingles is incredibly painful, and anyone with it certainly has my sympathy!

The following year it seemed as if everything that could go wrong did go wrong. My ME became considerably worse over just a few months due to the development of numerous problems, including thyroid problems, digestive problems and liver problems, all of which are still ongoing. As a result, since that time I have been severely affected by ME, with the additional development of further difficulties, including more doses of shingles, seizures and adrenal insufficiency.

As a brief aside, during that time in 1999 when everything was going wrong, I had a visit from a lady who attended a local charismatic church which promotes 'faith healing'. She came to tell me that she belonged to a prayer group which regularly prayed for me (for which I thanked her) and also to say that she had received a 'word from the Lord' that my time of illness was over and that I was now to be well. I had got to the stage of being more or less bed-bound, yet this lady, who was no doubt very well meaning but very misguided, came to tell me that my time of being ill was over. She was actually quite upset that I did not accept what she said as being from the Lord.

Why do I mention this? I have done so because, over the years, I have heard from so many people who have been caused much needless pain and distress by those who promote wrong teaching in this area. To cope with any long-term illness or disability is not easy. However, to be told that you are not well through your own fault, due to a lack of faith or something similar, is doubly hurtful and cruel.

I do believe that when a person is ill it is right to pray for healing. Indeed, it would be rather odd not to do so. If a person is not healed, it does not mean that to pray for his or her healing is wrong; rather, it means that, in addition to praying that the person might be well, we should also pray that he or she will know God's help and strength to cope day by day. God in His mercy can and does heal people, if it is His will, but it is not always His will to do so.

Back to 1999. Having spent the previous few years at least able to get out a little locally, even though I couldn't walk any distance, I was now having to adjust to being mainly house-bound and spending much of my time in bed. The times when I did struggle to go out were mainly for medical appointments. As I hadn't had any benefit from either the herbal or homeopathic treatments which I tried years earlier, I then saw a doctor who specialized in nutritional medicine. Straight away he became certain that the vaccines had caused liver damage—and blood tests carried out clearly showed evidence that I did indeed have liver damage. Medication helped a little with the pain from the damage, but it didn't actually fix it; unfortunately, I was unable to tolerate most of the medication recommended. The main benefit from seeing this particular doctor was that the results of the tests he carried out have proved to be useful as evidence when trying to fill in forms for disability benefits!

Sometime later I saw an endocrine specialist. I knew that I had thyroid problems for which I would be on medication for life, but although I suspected that my adrenal glands were not working as they should, I had never been tested for such problems. Again, the results were clear and I was diagnosed with adrenal insufficiency, for which I have to take daily medication. However, the overall results were not those I had hoped for. More problems were being found and medication tried, but my health continued to deteriorate.

A consultant who specialized in the autonomic nervous system carried out extensive tests a few years later and, as previously, numerous physical abnormalities showed up, particularly regarding the control (or lack of it) of my heart rate and blood pressure, and partly explaining the problems with my sense of balance. These findings have also proved to be useful with the disability benefits people, but no treatment was offered. Indeed, it was this doctor who, after doing some tests, said that the vaccines had undoubtedly caused brain stem damage which could not be reversed, and which would account for my autonomic nervous system not working properly.

There was one thing that puzzled all of the doctors I saw—and I saw quite a few of them. The number of physical abnormalities found increased, but normally, if a person has, for example, some kind of thyroid disorder, there is a family history of such problems. However, in my case, there was no family history of others in the family who had had problems in any way similar to my own. In many ways this was a relief, as I wouldn't wish ME on anyone, but it is also a puzzle!

Since 1999 there were a few months here and there when I experienced some short-term, small improvements, but overall it was downhill health-wise. I was now pretty much house-bound and I had to spend the vast majority of my time in bed, with increasing pain and exhaustion. It is well over ten years since I was last well enough to attend a church service. With spending my life mainly in one room, and the feeling that the walls around me were shrinking, I became more dependent on using email and the Internet—things I could do without having to get up! I was therefore delighted when churches began live-streaming their services online. Of course, for those who are well enough, there is no substitute for being able to attend services, but for those of us who can't do so, watching live comes in at a very good second best!

It is widely recognized that MS (Multiple Sclerosis) can follow different paths in different people. The same is true of ME—my illness being clearly progressive, becoming more complicated and more restrictive as the years go by. I often feel like a spectator watching from the sidelines as life passes by: watching world events happening on the news, being unable to attend church and family gatherings, most notably the wedding of my brother Tim to Lois in 2009. Yes, there was much joy surrounding the event, but there was great disappointment personally at not being able to be there.

A big change came for me and my parents in June 2012 when we moved from North Somerset to County Down in Northern Ireland. With Mum and Dad getting older, me unwell with severe ME, and after much talking and praying, we felt that the time was right to move to be near Tim and

Chapter 9

Lois, who lived in County Down (Lois comes from Belfast). Our home near Bristol sold within forty-eight hours of us contacting an estate agent—which was a bit of a shock to the system. However, the actual move, by road and ferry, was something of a challenge with my having severe ME—but God undertook, and we were thankful for the prayers and support of many friends both in the UK and further afield.

Since the move, Mum and Dad have settled well into a local church which is less than two miles from where we live and where they are now members. Tim and Lois belong to the same church and their home is also less than two miles from ours. Mum and Dad were able to get out and about quite a bit after we moved, meaning that they got to know the area around us quickly.

From my point of view, however, it was a difficult time. Things went downhill health-wise after the move—which was not totally unexpected—but sadly I never picked up again as hoped. Rarely being well enough to leave home—apart from for a handful of medical appointments—meant that I didn't get to know the area where we live, and even now I still feel like a stranger here, not knowing the area and knowing only a small number of people. It's all very different from the fit and active teenager I used to be, or from the experienced nurse I hoped to have become by this time.

*God is our refuge and strength,
a very present help in trouble.*
(Psalm 46:1)

*Abnormalities of immune function,
hypothalamic and pituitary function,
neurotransmitter regulation and cerebral
perfusion have been found in patients with
[ME].*
(Dr David S. Bell, Instructor in Paediatrics, Harvard
Medical School, 'Chronic Fatigue Syndrome
Update: Findings Now Point to CNS Involvement',
Postgraduate Medicine 98, no. 6 [1994]: 73–81)

New challenges

To bring events right up to date, things have not improved over the last few years; in fact, they have quite simply got worse and more complicated.

Just before Christmas 2013, I suddenly developed severe pain in my lower abdomen. I put up with this for some weeks without knowing for sure what the problem was. Eventually, an urgent appointment with a gynaecologist resulted in various tests and scans. The results a few days later revealed numerous serious gynaecological 'women's' problems, some of which I was already aware of, and any one of which could by itself cause severe pain—although exactly why the pain came on so suddenly remains something of a mystery. The consultant told me that, based on the test results, she also could not rule out a diagnosis of ovarian cancer (and it has never actually been ruled out). She said that under normal circumstances she would recommend a full hysterectomy.

However, severe ME is definitely not 'normal circumstances', and I knew that I had a major problem: I was in no way well enough to undergo any surgery, let alone a big operation such as a hysterectomy. Fortunately, the consultant was very understanding (surprisingly so) and didn't put any pressure on me to have surgery or accept any particular treatment.

I knew that, in my situation, surgery was quite simply not an option, and neither were the various hormonal treatments that so often come with numerous side-effects—especially for those like me who have problems tolerating medication. Therefore, I was sure that any treatment would need to be natural—dietary/nutritional—an area I have been interested in and have studied from home over the years. One of the main problems with this kind of approach is that it is slow. There are no quick results. A lot of time and patience are needed (although the latter is not always forthcoming!), as well as being prepared to fine-tune the dietary changes and supplements as needed. Whilst all of these extra problems have taken their toll health-wise generally, since following my dietary/nutritional regime there have been some noticeable changes and improvements in the gynae problems—although there is definitely still quite a long way to go.

I have had some degree of pain every day for the last twenty-five years—ME is a very painful illness at times—but that which I have experienced during the last three and a half years has at times been extreme, on another level from anything I have ever known and had to deal with before. As a result, I have been virtually bed-bound. Even sitting to type became just too painful, so I have had to get used to typing on a small mobile device or tablet with a detachable keyboard (as I am doing now as I lie in bed).

The Bible makes it clear that, as Christians, we are involved in a spiritual battle (Ephesians 6:12), and these two years have also been a real battle for me from a Christian point of view, something I heard described in one sermon as being like going through a storm—and I certainly wouldn't disagree with that. The Scriptures describe the devil 'as a roaring lion … seeking whom he may devour' (1 Peter 5:8), and what better time to attack a Christian than when she is at her weakest and in so much pain that it is difficult to even think straight? I was left feeling that God was at a distance, that what I was going through was unreasonable, and that the many assurances and promises we find in Scripture were left unfulfilled. On top of that, it seemed that the more people prayed for me—and a lot of people have been praying—the worse things got! I can honestly say that the thought of cancer and dying didn't—and still doesn't—worry me; it was having to cope seemingly alone, and without the expected help, that was so hard.

However, God is faithful (Deuteronomy 7:9), He cannot fail (2 Timothy 2:13), and that which He has promised in His infallible Word, the Bible, cannot fail either. There were no flashing lights or fuzzy feelings, and I certainly don't have all the answers, but help and assurance gradually came, thanks to the wise counsel of a pastor via email, from the Bible, and from listening to hymns and sermons. At times, I think it comes down to 'raw faith', having to trust the Bible whether we feel anything or not, trusting that the way God leads us is the right way for us. As one pastor said, 'We trust God, even when we cannot trace Him.'

*A*h Lord GOD! *behold, thou hast made the heaven and the earth by thy great power and stretched-out arm, and there is nothing too hard for thee.*
(Jeremiah 32:17)

*T*he *worst cases have both an MS-like and an AIDS-like clinical appearance. The most difficult thing to treat is the severe pain. Most have abnormal neurological examination. 80% of cases are unable to work or attend school. We admit regularly to hospital with an inability to care for self.*
(Paul Cheney, Professor of Medicine, Capital University, USA, Testimony before the FDA Scientific Advisory Committee, 18 February 1993)

❝ Looking forward with ME

Despite being in my forties, I still live with my parents, both of whom are in their seventies and upon whom I remain very dependent. I live in an area that I do not really know and where I know very few people. Scary? Yes—and no.

As a Christian, I know that my future is secure—through no merit or works of my own. My salvation is all of God through the Lord Jesus Christ, 'Who his own self bare our sins in his own body on the tree' (1 Peter 2:24). I don't have all the answers. I don't know what will happen in the coming months and years, and I am naturally concerned about the future. But I do have a Saviour, and I know that my future is safe in His hands.

However, it is still not easy from day to day—and the Bible nowhere promises that it will be! At numerous times during these last three and a half years I felt that I had reached 'the verge of Jordan'. Every day is a real struggle. I can see how things will be in the long term (i.e. heaven!), but I can't at present see how things will work out in the short term. Yet I have become increasingly aware that I am in God's hands, and that is the safest place to be; therefore I have to trust Him to provide. I also know that a day is coming when the Lord Jesus will return. I will then see my Saviour and have a new body, one that works and is not falling apart!

Do you have that assurance? When in this world, the Lord Jesus lived a perfect, righteous life, in obedience to His Father—the life that we, because of our sin, could never live. He died on the cross, bearing the eternal punishment of sin for all those who put their trust in Him. He rose from the grave, conquering sin, death and hell.

The Bible states that 'God so loved the world, that he gave his only begotten Son, that whosoever believeth in him should not perish, but have everlasting life' (John 3:16).

Chapter 11

For those whom God has saved by His grace, we look forward to the time when 'God shall wipe away all tears from their eyes; and there shall be no more death, neither sorrow, nor crying, neither shall there be any more pain; for the former things are passed away' (Revelation 21:4).

All the way my Saviour leads me:
What have I to ask beside?
Can I doubt His tender mercy,
Who through life has been my Guide?
Heavenly peace, divinest comfort,
Here by faith in Him to dwell!
For I know, whate'er befall me,
Jesus doeth all things well.

All the way my Saviour leads me:
Cheers each winding path I tread;
Gives me grace for every trial,
Feeds me with the living bread.
Though my weary steps may falter,
And my soul may thirsting be,
Gushing from the Rock before me,
Lo! a spring of joy I see.

All the way my Saviour leads me;
O, the fullness of His love!
Perfect rest to me is promised
In my Father's house above.
When my spirit, clothed immortal,
Wings its flight to realms of day,
This my song through endless ages:
Jesus led me all the way.

(Fanny J. Crosby, 1820–1915)

*J*esus said unto her, I am the resurrection, and the
life: he that believeth in me, though he were dead,
yet shall he live.
(John 11:25)

*M*any of the documented abnormalities involve
the central and autonomic nervous systems.
In my experience, most sceptics are unaware of the
extensive literature citing such abnormalities and
become less sceptical upon reading it.
(Professor Anthony Komaroff, *Nature Reviews
Neuroscience*, September 2011)

Some basic information about ME

ME stands for Myalgic Encephalomyelitis. It is in reality a multi-system failure, and has been classed by the World Health Organization as a neurological condition since 1969 (reference ICD-10 G93.3). It brings with it a post-exertional malaise, muscle pain and weakness, flu-like symptoms, digestive problems, exhaustion which is not alleviated by rest, as well as many other problems which can vary from person to person. It affects every system and part of the body, including the central and autonomic nervous systems, muscles, and immune, endocrine and digestive systems; it can be fatal.

Many people currently refer to the illness as CFS—Chronic Fatigue Syndrome—but this is unfortunate as, firstly, CFS is really an 'umbrella' term covering a number of fatigue syndromes and conditions. Secondly, the term CFS does tend to trivialize the illness by giving the impression that fatigue is the only problem faced by those who have it, which is certainly not the case. After all, 'fatigue' is a symptom, not an illness, and there are many people for whom chronic fatigue is a problem who do not have ME, such as those with MS or undergoing cancer treatment. ME is definitely not simply the 'chronic fatigue' wrongly portrayed as ME by much of the media and, sadly, also by the medical profession.

Research has shown numerous physical biomedical abnormalities in people with ME, including the following:

- *Immune system:* chronic immune activation and dysfunction, evidence of persistent viral infection, low natural killer cells
- *Brain and central nervous system:* objective measurement of dysfunction deficits in working memory, concentration, information processing, white and grey matter abnormalities, abnormal neuro-genetic expression

- *Endocrine system:* impaired activation of the hypothalamic-pituitary-adrenal (HPA) axis
- *Muscular:* structural and biochemical abnormalities, including impaired muscle recovery after exercise
- *Heart and circulatory system:* hypoperfusion, impaired vascular control, low blood volume
- *Others:* gastrointestinal dysfunction, including food intolerance; mitochondrial dysfunction, including abnormal mitochondrial associated gene expression

The following are some of the main symptoms of ME:

- *Exhaustion and post-exertional malaise:* Exhaustion is a principal symptom of ME, is experienced by all sufferers, and must not previously have been a problem. It is caused by trivially small amounts of exertion—physical or mental—compared with before the onset of the illness. Activity can put someone in bed for days or, if overdone, can cause a major relapse. It produces a post-exertional malaise, accompanied by muscle pain and weakness, that can begin soon after activity or be delayed by as much as seventy-two hours, which can make planning anything very difficult. The exhaustion in ME is severe, disabling and totally unlike that experienced by healthy people. Some have described it as being totally drained of energy and 'having their plug pulled out'. Unlike normal tiredness, it is not helped by exercise and would be made worse by it.
- *Neurological and cognitive problems:* such as impairment of concentration and short-term memory; mixing-up of words; difficulty processing information; disturbed, unrefreshing sleep, with a lack of normal, restorative sleep; balance problems; sensory disturbances (e.g. hypersensitivity to light and sound).
- *Unpredictable fluctuation of symptoms:* from day to day, or within a day. This can mean not feeling tired all the time, but it is common to feel ill all the time! Symptoms can be exacerbated by doing too much and not managing the condition properly.

Other symptoms include muscle pain (which can be severe) and muscle weakness; multi-joint pain, normally without swelling; clinical/laboratory evidence of viral infection, with sore throats and painful lymph nodes; poor temperature control (sweating or shivering); altered sleep patterns; chest pain (which should be investigated if frequent and/or severe); abnormalities to the heart rate and rhythm, including palpitations; visual disturbances; problems with digestion similar to Irritable Bowel Syndrome; severe migraine-type headaches; and generally feeling unwell.

ME usually has a sudden onset following a viral illness (e.g. flu, gastroenteritis), but it can also follow the use of pesticides/organophosphates or a vaccination—as in my case.

For further information about ME, please see the 'Latest News' and 'Medical Articles' pages on my website On Eagles Wings: A Christian Perspective on ME: www.oneagleswings.me.uk.

The following charities may also be of help:

- The 25% ME Group, for those with severe ME: www.25megroup. org/
- The TYMES Trust, especially for children and young people with ME: www.tymestrust.org/
- Invest in ME, an independent charity campaigning for biomedical research into ME: www.investinme.org/

To download and read the many articles about ME written by Prof. Malcolm Hooper and Margaret Williams since 1986, please go to www. margaretwilliams.me.

*F*ear thou not; for I am with thee: be not dismayed;
for I am thy God: I will strengthen thee; yea, I will
help thee; yea, I will uphold thee with the right hand of
my righteousness.
(Isaiah 41:10)

*M*E is characterized by an
inability to produce sufficient
energy on demand.
(2003 Canadian Consensus Guidelines)

69 Some thoughts on caring

This article was written in January 2012 and is included here in case it might be of help to some.

Having been asked to write on the subject of 'needing care', I wasn't really sure where to begin! Therefore what follows are simply a few thoughts that I have had on the subject of caring for and supporting those who have long-term health problems.

Just to give a few details about where I am coming from: I have been ill with ME (Myalgic Encephalomyelitis, a neurological condition) since February 1991. I had been studying to be a nurse at the time, but suddenly became ill following a Hepatitis B vaccination that I was required to have for my training, and I have been ill ever since. For the first eight years or so I was moderately affected by my illness, but since 1999 I have had severe ME and my health continues to gradually deteriorate. I am mainly housebound and have to spend much of my time resting. How thankful I am for my laptop computer and email and the Internet! I live with my parents, both of whom are past retirement age, and am very dependent on them; this is obviously a matter of concern as Mum and Dad get older.

Over the years I have listened to many sermons and read many books and articles on the subject of suffering and related issues, some good, some not so good! I guess a lot depends upon whether or not the speaker or author has had personal experience of suffering or of caring for someone close to them who is unwell or disabled in some way. However, even if they have done so, for those who are ill 'suffering is a very lonely path, cut off from others but longing that someone would understand' (Barbara Edwards).

When unable to go out very much and having to spend a lot of the time looking at the same four walls, it is easy to lose touch with reality. Things that are 'normal' for most people, such as having jobs, getting married, having children, and so on, can seem abnormal and well out of reach. There are feelings of guilt, of being a burden on those who care for you, knowing how much your illness affects and limits their lives as well as your own. Trying to remain positive and cheerful as much as possible is no doubt a help to those who care—but it is also something of a challenge when feeling ill and in pain! For those of us who are ill and single, another problem is of course that of loneliness, of being cut off from other people, of not having a husband or wife—and it is particularly hard when all those around you appear to be getting married, settling down, and having families!

However, 'the times we find ourselves having to wait on others may be the perfect opportunities to train ourselves to wait on God' (Joni Eareckson Tada). It is important to remember that God makes no mistakes. We may not understand why things happen to us, and we may not find it easy to have to 'give in' and swallow our pride and let others do things for us, but for those of us who are Christians, we know that we have a Sovereign God and that our lives are in His hands. As Calvin put it, 'we are not afflicted by chance, but through the infallible providence of God'.

There are certainly lessons to be learned when ill: 'sickness takes us aside and sets us alone with God, and with all the props removed, we learn to lean on God alone' (Horatius Bonar). We come to realize that there is nothing that this world offers that can ultimately give us the comfort and strength that we need to cope from day to day. We also come to see that, from a practical point of view, we need to let others care for and help us, to do things which we would usually do for ourselves—whether that be helping with personal needs, giving a lift to medical appointments, doing some shopping (although much can now be done online!), or whatever.

For Christians who are involved in caring for a fellow Christian who is ill, don't forget that the comfort which a Christian can give to another Christian is unique. Non-Christian relatives and friends can of course offer help and support, and it is much appreciated, but it is only Christians who can bring encouragement and minister to their fellow believers at a spiritual level. We are told to 'rejoice with them that do rejoice, and weep with them that weep' (Romans 12:15).

There is, of course, a sense in which real comfort in the midst of suffering can only come to us from God Himself. We have great consolation in

Christ. He knows our sorrows, He understands what we are going through. We have the Holy Spirit as our Comforter, to sustain and strengthen us when we feel we are floundering. We have the Scriptures. We know that 'all things work together for good to them that love God' and that 'the sufferings of this present time are not worthy to be compared with the glory which shall be revealed in us' (Romans 8:28, 18). Times of suffering and affliction provide opportunities for us to witness and to glorify God. To quote Horatius Bonar again: 'What a God-honouring thing to see a struggling, sorrowing child of earth cleave fast to God, calmly trusting Him, happy and at rest in the midst of storm and suffering.'

Back to caring: For someone who has always enjoyed good health, the idea of trying to help a person with a chronic health problem or disability that has lasted for many years and that we know nothing about may seem a bit daunting. What should be done? How can we sympathize with someone if we have never experienced their particular problem? Will we cause offence by saying the wrong thing? These are natural concerns, but should not put people off from trying!

The vast majority of the people with long-term health difficulties that I have come across over the years would be absolutely delighted to have someone get in touch with them and show some support and concern. If you don't know what to do or say, ask! If you know that a person has a particular illness or disability, do a bit of reading around the subject, look up support groups on the Internet, look out for leaflets in your local doctor's surgery. The fact that you have shown an interest, learnt a little about the problem and gone to the effort of getting in touch will be greatly appreciated and will be a real encouragement to the sufferer.

When ill, receiving a letter, phone call, email or even a short visit from a fellow Christian means such a lot—and I am sure that it is virtually impossible for those who are healthy to realize how much doing just a small thing like writing a little note can mean, resulting in many simply not bothering. However, I would urge you to bother, to go to the effort of sending a card or email, making a phone call, dropping in for a visit (but do phone first and don't stay for too long!); it means so much and is such a help and encouragement.

However, do be careful. Don't start something that you can't keep up. It's no good saying that you will call in once a week if you cannot do it in the long term. Chronic health problems are a 'long haul'. Far better to visit once a month and be able to stick at it over a number of months or years, than try calling every week only to find that you can't keep it up and so have to stop after just a few weeks.

When you visit someone with long-term health problems it is likely that they will be, to a greater or lesser extent, physically dependent on others to manage from day to day. However, it is important that the sufferer does not become spiritually dependent on any particular person—you mustn't become a 'spiritual prop'! It is important to be there to help them, but try to direct them to the Bible, to find their ultimate help and strength from God and His Word.

One other thing to bear in mind is that the person you are trying to help may feel rather useless due to their circumstances. They may have had to stop many of the things they used to do at home, at work and in the church. Do suggest to them that they maintain an interest in and pray for other people. Missionaries known to the church could be a particular focus for their prayers. Writing letters or emails to those working abroad (something that I have enjoyed doing for many years) can be encouraging on both sides, as can helping others with the same health problem. Also remind them not to underestimate what a powerful witness it can be to non-Christians to see someone coping with a long-term illness. J. C. Ryle commented that it is possible for those who are ill to 'honour God as much by patient suffering as they can by active work. It often shows more grace to sit still than it does to go to and fro, and perform great exploits'.

Be practical: try to think of things that you would find helpful if you were house-bound or bed-bound—for example, offering to help with shopping, cooking meals, giving lifts to doctors' and hospital appointments. If the person is well enough, just offering to take them out for a short drive is likely to be greatly appreciated. Going out even for a short time can give a tremendous boost.

Be spiritual: one of the hardest things that I have found, as a Christian, to cope with during my years of ill-health is the lack of Christian fellowship due to not being able to attend church very often. Listening to recordings of the ministry is to be recommended and is a great help, but being cut off from your Christian family is very hard.

Be encouraging: chronic ill-health is hard, especially in our society when we are used to the idea that if any health problem arises we can simply go to the doctor's and get a prescription to make us better!

Being long-term sick means that it is easy to lose touch with what is going on in the 'big, wide world'. Talk about normal things. Tell the person about your family, what's happening at the church, any interesting places you've visited. Don't expect the sick person to initiate the conversation; after all, they may not have been anywhere or done very much, meaning that it is not easy to start talking. At the same time, give them time to talk about whatever is on their mind.

You don't need to have experienced an illness in order to help and support someone with it. Be honest. Admit that you don't know much. Most people with a long-term problem know a lot about their condition and will be happy to fill you in on the details—probably in far more detail than you actually need or want to know!

Be forward-looking: it is always good to talk about heaven with those who are ill! Remember that this world is not our home; we are just a-passing through. Whether or not we will be healed in this life is unknown, but in heaven we will see our Saviour and we will be free from sin and from suffering. 'For the unbeliever, death is the end of all joys; for the believer, death is the end of all griefs' (Matthew Henry). Always be 'looking for that blessed hope, and the glorious appearing of the great God and our Saviour Jesus Christ' (Titus 2:13).

> For yonder a light shines eternal
> Which spreads through the valley of gloom;
> Lord Jesus, resplendent and regal,
> Drives fear far away from the tomb.
> Our God is the end of the journey,
> His pleasant and glorious domain;
> For there are the children of mercy,
> Who praise Him for Calvary's pain.
>
> (W. V. Higham, used by kind permission)

Hazel Stapleton, January 2012

For God so loved the world, that he gave his only begotten Son, that whosoever believeth in him should not perish, but have everlasting life.
(John 3:16)

⌒

For of him, and through him, and to him, are all things: to whom be glory for ever. Amen.
(Romans 11:36)

⌒

Visit the website
On Eagles Wings: A Christian Perspective on ME
www.oneagleswings.me.uk